The Health Status of Latinos in California

The California Endowment *and*
California HealthCare Foundation

April 1997

The California Endowment and California HealthCare
Foundation were established by Blue Cross of California

Published by The California Endowment and California HealthCare Foundation

April 1997

Woodland Hills, California

To order publications please call 818.703.3311 x503. Publications are made available to the public at no charge, however we ask that you limit your request to one (1) copy per publication.

Contents

Preface

Prior to the establishment of The California Endowment (TCE) and the California HealthCare Foundation (CHF), Blue Cross of California commissioned five papers on the health status of California's public. TCE and CHF subsequently assumed responsibility for the project and completed the production of these five papers for public dissemination.

Each of the five papers focuses on a significant ethnic/racial population in California: African Americans; Whites; Latinos; American Indians; and Asian and Pacific Islander Americans. The goal of these papers is to go beyond epidemiology in order to explain or hypothesize factors that gave rise to these data and to better understand how health impacts the content and context of people's lives. Although the authors were asked to follow a standard format, wide latitude was granted to ensure the authors' unique voices in making the statistics more meaningful. For example, some authors emphasized how past historical experiences shaped a population's health today, others focused on the impact of financial and non-financial barriers to care and some honed in on the challenges facing certain populations and made recommendations for change.

Each report is available separately, but we hope you will consider reviewing the set of papers to gain a deeper perspective on the challenges that remain to reduce the variation in health status among the different ethnic/racial populations that together make California the most diverse, fascinating, and unique state in the nation.

Dana E. McMurtry
Director, Health Policy Research

The California Endowment

Introduction

Today, almost one out of every three Californians is Latino. Of children born in the state, nearly one out of every two are Latino. In the memory of many adults in the state, Latinos appear to have suddenly grown from a small minority to a sizeable portion of the state.

This growth has not been sudden, there is a historical pattern to this growth. More important, there are implications for many facets of the state's activities including: its economy; its educational efforts; the political debates; and, of course, the health of the public of the state.

This paper provides an overview of the health of the Latino population, its implications for those interested in health policy, programs and services, and for the California of the 21st century.

There were nine million Latinos in the state of California in the mid-1990s. To put this number in perspective, the Latino population of this state was larger than the entire population of the state of Ohio or Michigan, not small or insignificant states by any stretch of the imagination. Any effort to effect fundamental changes in the health of the California public must take into account this large and growing particular public.

1. Changes in the State's Health and Its Public

Earlier in this century, the population of California tended to die of acute, infectious causes; tuberculosis, pneumonia, influenza, diphtheria and polio were troublesome causes of death as recently as 1940.

With both economic growth in the state (which allowed for easier access to sanitation and clean water) and the development of immunizations (such as the Salk and Sabine vaccines which virtually eliminated polio) the causes of death changed to "style of life" diseases, which were more the products of how one lived, ate, drank, smoked and moved than exposure to infectious agents. Whereas in an earlier time the health of the public could be fundamentally affected almost purely by technical medical and public health measures enjoyed by a passive public, now the major causes of death require a more active public involvement.

The change from infectious causes of death to style of life is typical for industrializing and modernizing societies. What is unique to California is that this change occurred within one population, an essentially white non-Hispanic population. Yet as the 20th century draws to a close, that population is becoming a minority in the state. The illness, disease and death processes will exercise their outcomes on a population that is increasingly diverse.

A large portion of that diversity is due to the growth of the Latino public. The health and medical ends of reducing levels of disease and increasing levels of wellness now depend, to a large extent, on the lifestyles of the Latino public.

2. Contours and Features of the Health of the Latino Public

This population presents some health contours that may seem surprising to those unfamiliar with Latino mortality, morbidity and services utilization. Although this population exhibits many classic risk factors—low income; low education levels; low access to care—these do not seem to be highly associated with overall poor health outcomes. Instead, Latinos generally exhibit low death rates (crude and age-adjusted), good birth outcomes, and comparatively light usage of inpatient services. However, against this generally positive profile must be contrasted high levels of morbidity, especially in diseases that are more public health in nature, rather than medical. In addition, for some selected causes of death, Latinos have comparatively high rates.

Death rates give a good place to start to understand the effects of a large and growing Latino public on the health profile of the state.

A. Crude vs. Age-adjusted Rates

There are two primary ways of presenting death rate data. Crude rates represent the number of deaths that occur in every 100,000 population. Thus, in the state overall, the Latino crude death rate in 1993 was 288.3 per 100,000, which means that for every 100,000 Latinos in the state, 288.3 of them died in that year. The state's overall death rate was 693.9 per 100,000, which meant that of every 100,000 Californians, 693.9 died in that same year, *Figure 1.*

Figure 1.

Comparative Death Rates For All Causes, Crude and Age-adjusted, California, 1993

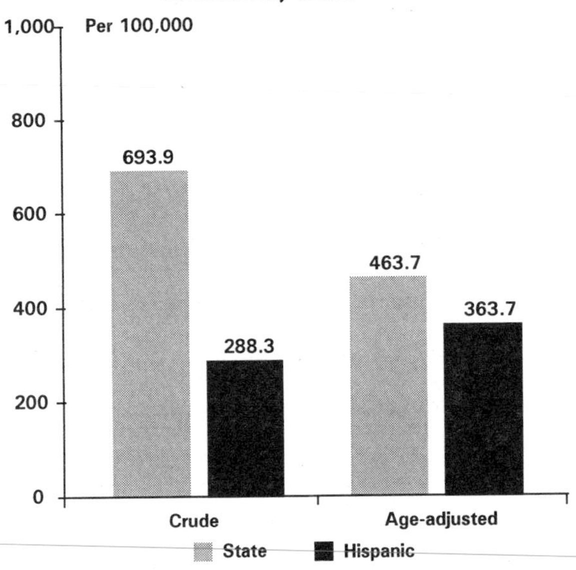

Source: California Department of Health Services, Death Records.
California Department of Finance, 1993 Population Estimates for California Counties.

It should be noted that the Latino crude death rate is much lower than the state's overall rate. In part, this is due to the fact that the Latino population is much younger than the state's overall population, younger people generally have lower death rates than older people. At times, it is useful to know what the Latino rate would be if it were not so young.

There are many ways to do this. One common method is to "age adjust" the death rates, by artificially changing the age structure of the populations so that they have the same proportion of young people and old people. Age adjusting means making the Latino population artificially older than it really is, and making the state's population younger than it really is, so that death rates can be compared without the effects of age. When the age adjustment is made, the Latino age-adjusted death rate is 363.7, lower than the state age-adjusted rate of 463.7.

In this project, it was noted that there are three categories of death rates:

- Causes of death for which Latino both crude and age-adjusted death rates were lower than the state's;
- Causes of death where Latino crude rates were lower than the state's, but the age-adjusted rates were higher;
- Causes of death where Latino both crude and age-adjusted rates were higher than the state's.

B. Lower Crude and Age-adjusted Rates

Heart

The number one cause of death in the country and in the state is heart disease. Overall, of every 100,000 Californians, 216.1 died of heart disease in 1993. This rate, however, varies greatly by ethnicity. For Latinos, the crude death rate is quite a bit lower at 65.4 per 100,000, the Latino crude death rate is less than one-third that of the state, *Figure 2*.

Figure 2.

Top Ten Causes of Hispanic Origin Death, Crude Rate, California, 1993

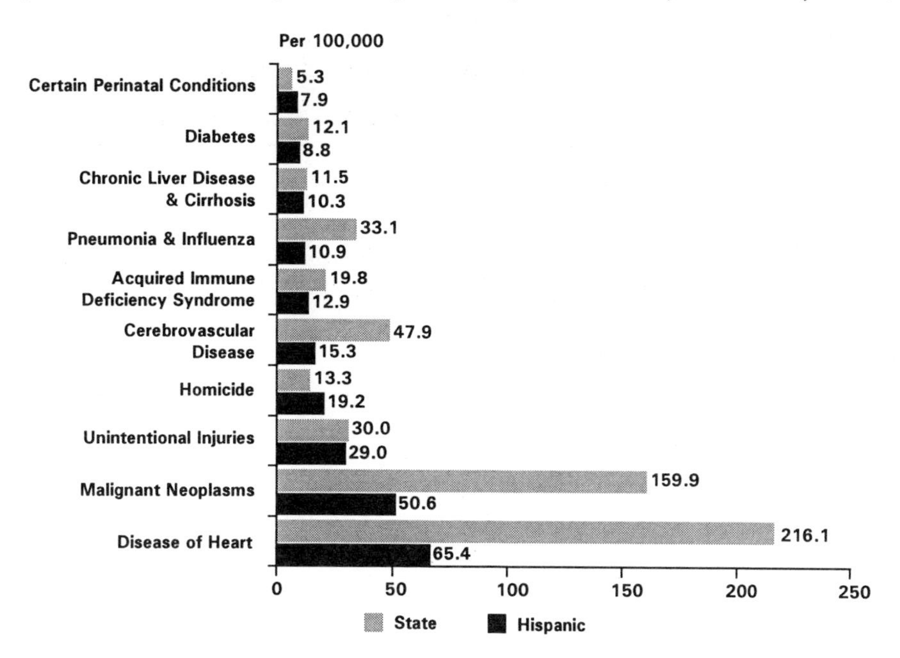

Source: California Department of Health Services, Death Records. California Department of Finance, 1993 Population Estimates for California Counties.

As will be seen in *2.G. Hospital Services* section, this lower crude death rate translates into a lower rate of hospitalizations for heart related DRGs (Diagnosis-Related Groups) and lower expenditure patterns for heart related DRGs.

This lower crude rate is in part a function of a younger Latino age structure. The age-adjusted rate removes this age differential. The age-adjusted state level death rate is 123.6 deaths per 100,000; the Latino rate is still lower, at 90.9 deaths per 100,000, *Figure 3*.

Figure 3.

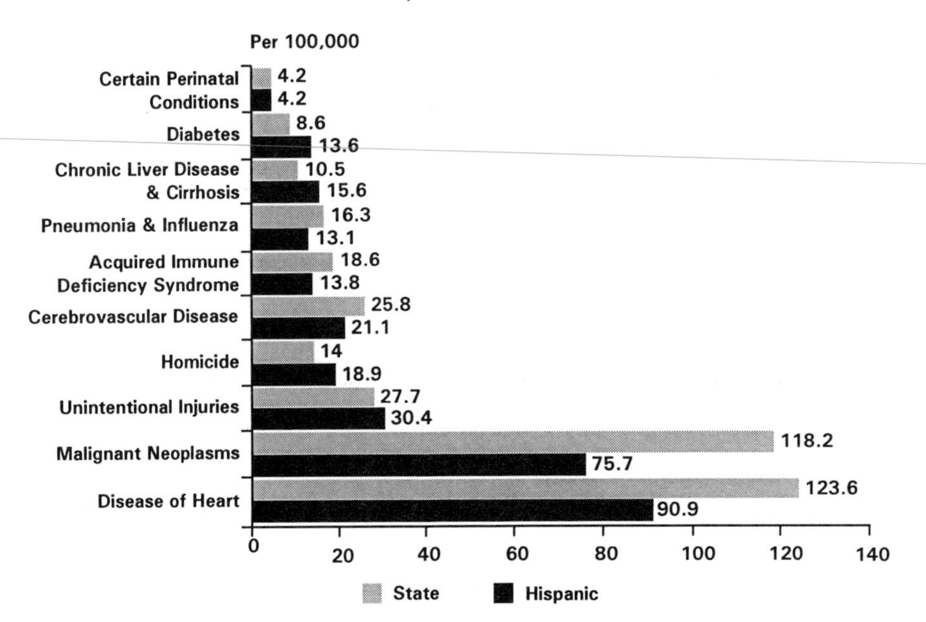

Source: California Department of Health Services, Death Records. California Department of Finance, 1993 Population Estimates for California Counties.

Cancer

The number two cause of death in the country and in the state are cancers. Overall, in the state, 159.9 Californians per 100,000 died of malignant neoplasms in 1993. The Latino crude death rate was less than one-third the state rate, at 50.6 per 100,000.

The age-adjusted rate for the state was 118.2 deaths per 100,000. For Latinos, the age-adjusted rate was 75.7.

Stroke

The number three cause of death in the country and in the state, was stroke. The crude death rate for the state was 47.9 deaths per 100,000 Californians. The Latino crude death rate was about one-third that of the state, at 15.3 per 100,000.

After removing the effects of age, the state's age-adjusted rate was 25.8 per 100,000 and the Latino age-adjusted rate was 21.1

Pneumonia and Influenza

The state crude death rate for pneumonia and influenza was 33.1 deaths per 100,000. For Latinos, the rate was 10.9 deaths per 100,000. When adjusted for age, the state rate was 16.3, and the Latino rate was 13.1.

Acquired Immune Deficiency Syndrome (AIDS)

The state crude death rate was 19.8 per 100,000. For Latinos, the crude death rate was 12.9. The age-adjusted rates were 18.6 for the state and 13.8 for Latinos.

C. Lower Crude and Higher Age-adjusted Rates

There were some causes of death which tend to be associated more with younger populations than older populations. When age adjustments are made, the Latino age-adjusted rates are higher than the state age-adjusted rates.

Unintentional Injuries

The state crude rate was 30.0 deaths per 100,000, and the Latino crude rate was 29.0 per 100,000. When adjusted for age, the Latino rate (30.4) is higher than the state rate (27.7).

Diabetes

At a crude level, the state death rate due to diabetes is 12.1 per 100,000, higher than the Latino crude rate of 8.8. However, when adjusted for age, the Latino rate of 13.6 is higher than the age-adjusted state rate of 8.6 per 100,000.

Chronic Liver Diseases and Cirrhosis

The state crude death rate of 11.5 is higher than the Latino crude rate of 10.3. The state age-adjusted rate of 10.5 is lower than the Latino age-adjusted rate of 15.6 deaths per 100,000.

D. Higher Crude and Higher Age-adjusted Death Rates

There are some causes of death for which the Latino rates, both crude and age-adjusted, are higher than the state rates.

Homicides

While the state crude homicide rate is 13.3 deaths per 100,000, the Latino crude rate is 19.2. When the adjustment for age is made, this pattern continues to hold, with the state age-adjusted rate of 14.0, lower than the Latino age-adjusted rate of 18.9.

Certain Perinatal Conditions

The state crude death rate of 5.3 was lower than the Latino rate of 7.9 deaths per 100,000. Once the age adjustment is made, the state rate is 4.2, the Latino rate is 4.2 deaths per 100,000.

E. Birth Outcomes

Prenatal care

Access to prenatal care may be seen as a surrogate indicator of overall access to health care services. Over the past few years, there has been an effort to expand access to prenatal care. During 1993, a lower percent of expectant Latinas (females) received prenatal care during the first trimester (68.2%) as compared to the state average (76.1%). This is a long-standing pattern, from 1982 to 1993, Latinas have consistently been less likely than the state norm to receive first trimester prenatal care, *Figure 4*.

Figure 4.

First Trimester Prenatal Care, California, 1982–1993

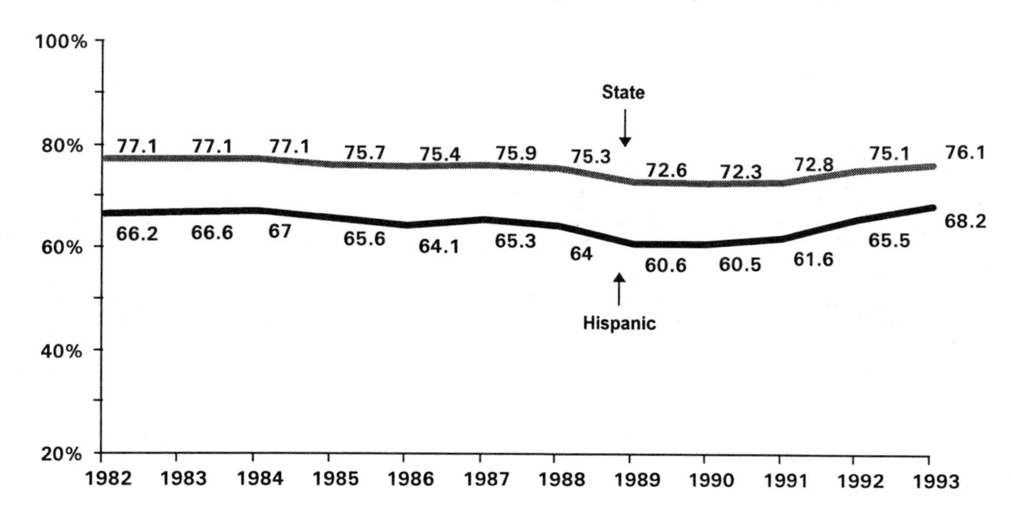

Source: California Department of Health Services, Health Information and Strategic Planning Center for Health Statistics Planning and Data Analysis Section

Low Birth Weight Babies

A major risk factor for survival in the first year of life is birth weight. Babies with a low birth weight (less than 2500 grams) are at higher risk for early death than those of higher birth weight (2500 grams or more).

In 1993, Latinas had a lower percent of low birth weight babies (5.4% of Latino live births were of low birth weight) as compared to the state figure (6.0%) of live births being of low birth weight. This pattern is fairly consistent from 1982 to 1993 as shown in *Figure 5*. Similar patterns have been seen nationally (Becerra, et al., 1991[1]).

Figure 5.

Low Birth Weight, California, 1982–1993

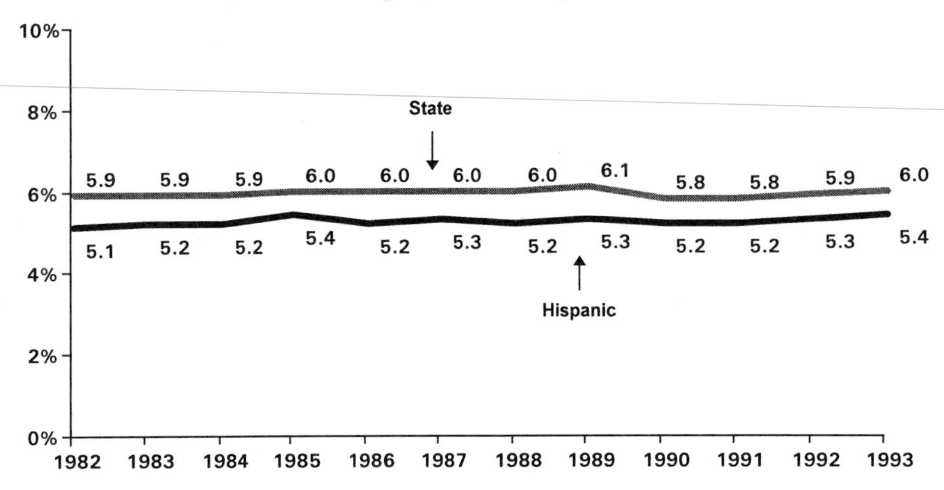

Source: California Department of Health Services, Health Information and Strategic Planning Center for Health Statistics Planning and Data Analysis Section

Infant Mortality

Infant mortality is the result of many factors, including access to prenatal care as well as mother's behavior (drinking, smoking, drug use, diet). This must be borne in mind when interpreting Latino infant mortality outcomes. In 1993, Latinos had a lower infant mortality (6.4 deaths per 1,000 live births) as compared to the state average (6.8 deaths per 1,000 live births).

This is a long-standing pattern, as seen in *Figure 6*, where Latino infant mortality has consistently been lower than the state figure for the ten-year period 1982–1992. Similar patterns have been reported at the national level (Becerra, et al., 1991[2]).

Figure 6.

Infant Mortality, California, 1982–1993

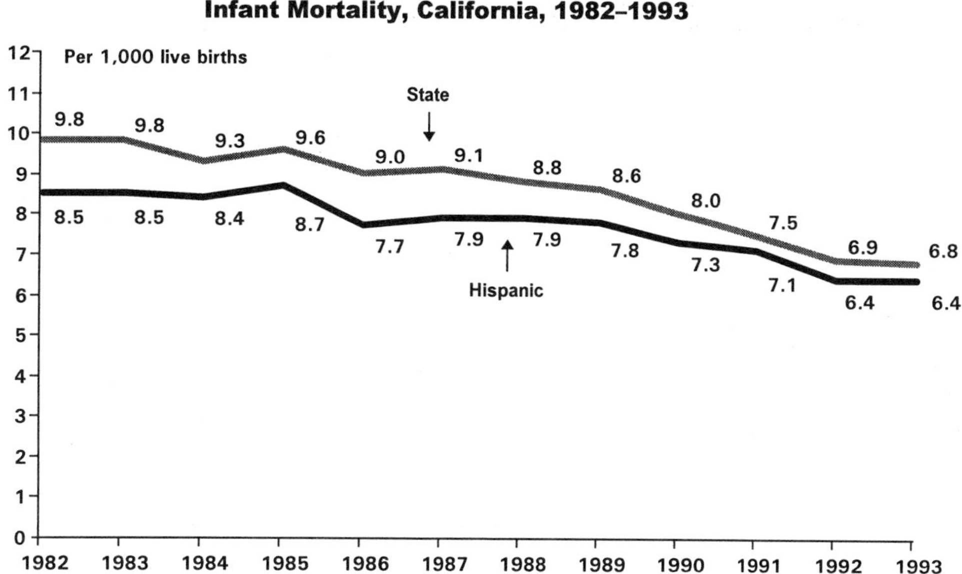

Source: California Department of Health Services, Health Information and Strategic Planning Center for Health Statistics Planning and Data Analysis Section

These infant mortality figures should *not* be interpreted to mean that access to prenatal care is not an issue for Latinos. Preliminary data from a number of studies indicate that Latinas are less likely to smoke, drink or use drugs than non-Latinas when pregnant (Vega, et al., 1993[3]), which may explain some of the seeming anomaly between low access to prenatal care and yet low infant mortality.

One may only imagine what the birth outcomes might be if the naturally occurring healthy behaviors were linked to adequate access to care.

F. Morbidity

As recently as 1940, diseases such as tuberculosis, pneumonia and influenza, diphtheria and polio were among the most worrisome causes of disease and death. With the development of statewide control efforts, and the application of modern medical technology, the effects of communicable diseases—tuberculosis, measles, polio and the like—have changed from being some of the significant causes of death to being illnesses that are inconvenient, but are no longer major killers.

However, the maintenance of these diseases as comparative irritants instead of the killers they were only two generations ago requires constant surveillance, education, communication, cooperation and activity in a public, organized fashion.

While the Latino public enjoys a fairly strong profile in terms of death rates and causes when compared to the state profile, the same cannot be said for communicable diseases. Latino rates for many communicable diseases are quite a bit higher than the state norm, indicating a lack of linkage between this public and the health programs designed to protect this public's health. These diseases, if left unattended, could attain epidemic proportions in fairly short order.

The most serious communicable diseases for the Latino public in 1992 were:

Tuberculosis

Once a scourge thought conquered, tuberculosis has made a strong reappearance in the Latino public. The Latino incidence rate of 24.1 per 100,000 is about 40% higher than the state rate of 17.2, *Figure 7.*

Figure 7.

Communicable Diseases, California, 1992

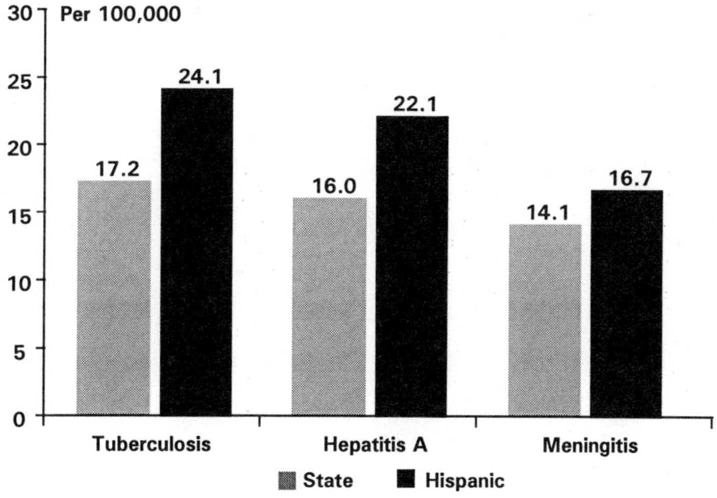

Per 100,000

	State	Hispanic
Tuberculosis	17.2	24.1
Hepatitis A	16.0	22.1
Meningitis	14.1	16.7

Source: California Department of Health Services

Immigrant Latinos are far more prone to suffer from tuberculosis than U.S.-born Latinos. To give an idea of the disparity, when the 1992 number of cases is converted to rates using 1990 Census data (the most recent available which distinguishes between U.S.-born and Immigrant Latino), the U.S. Latino rate is 13.1 cases per 100,000, while the Immigrant Latino rate is 44.4, *Figure 8.*

Figure 8.

Tuberculosis, U.S. and Immigrant, California, 1992

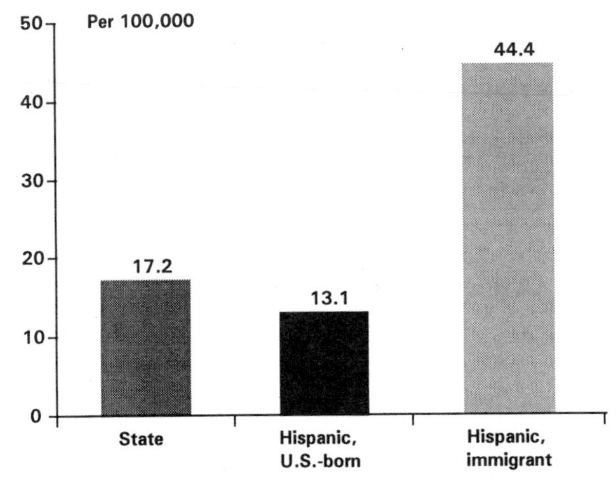

Source: California Department of Health Services

Hepatitis A

This disease is most commonly seen in young children. Not surprisingly, the Latino rate of 22.1 cases per 100,000 is about 38% higher than the state rate of 16.0.

Meningitis

A disease most often seen in children, the Latino rate of 16.7 cases per 100,000 is higher than the state rate of 14.1.

G. Sexually Transmitted Diseases

HIV/AIDS

The AIDS incidence case for Latinos differs from the national Latino profile in two important aspects. First, the overall incidence among California Latinos of 26.8 cases per 100,000 experienced in 1993 is lower than the state figure of 36.8, *Figure 9*. Outside of California, the Latino rate is higher than the non-Latino rate. Second, the major mode of transmission is sexual activity, unlike the Latino population outside of California in which the major mode of transmission is through shared injection needle usage.

Figure 9.

Sexually Transmitted Diseases, California, 1992

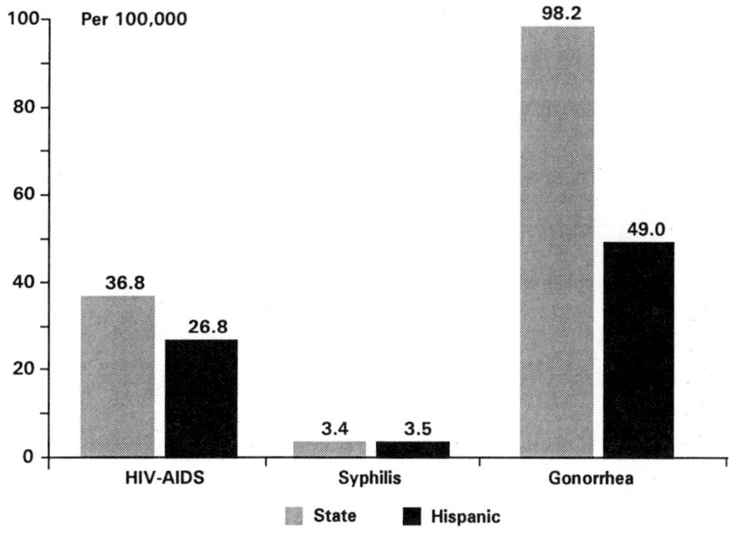

Per 100,000
100
80
60
40
20
0
36.8
26.8
3.4
3.5
98.2
49.0
HIV-AIDS
Syphilis
Gonorrhea
State
Hispanic

Source: California Department of Health Services, Office of AIDS, STD Control Branch

Syphilis

The Latino rate of 3.5 cases per 100,000 is slightly higher than the state figure of 3.4.

Gonorrhea

The Latino incidence rate of 49.0 cases per 100,000 is lower than the state rate of 98.2.

H. Services Utilization

Patterns of services utilization are difficult to discern. There is relatively good information about the use of hospitals, for every hospital discharge must be reported to the state. However, this is only half the services utilization picture. In 1993, on average, 7.5% of the nation's population was hospitalized for any reason (National Center for Health Statistics, 1994[4]). Most medical care is sought in ambulatory settings, nationally 78.6% of the population saw a doctor at least once during 1993. This care is sought in a variety of settings (doctors' offices, private *clinicas medicas*, county facilities and community clinics) and does not need to be reported to any agency.

In an ironic way, while relatively few people are hospitalized, the costs are enormous, and there is a great deal of information about these relatively rare occurrences. The source of care that most people use, ambulatory care in a variety of settings, is less expensive, yet comparatively little is known about it.

Even less is known of Latino utilization of ambulatory care. Yet, the emerging health profile is intriguing. The profile thus far suggests a population that might be well-suited to an ambulatory care approach. This is a population with comparatively low death rates for heart disease, cancer, stroke, and fairly good birth outcomes, yet there is a high incidence of communicable disease whose prevention and treatment can be provided in an ambulatory setting. The hospitalization data provide another piece to the puzzle and will be the focus of analysis here.

Medical care use is driven by two factors, *need* and *demand*. Crudely defined, demand is what the patient expects to receive (or is led to expect), while need is what the patient requires medically. There is growing opinion that demand is in turn driven by adequacy of health insurance coverage, with better covered patients expecting more care than those less well covered. Need is seen more as the product of a patient's lifestyle, including exposure to pathogens, diet, exercise, social support, education and surveillance.

The hospital utilization profiles of Latinos are sufficiently out of the ordinary as to create a desire for more in-depth understanding of demand versus need not only in this public, but in the greater California public.

Low Bed Days

When measured by bed days generated over a year per 1,000 persons, Latinos use hospital services less than the state average. In 1993, 1,000 Latinos generated 400.4 bed days; the state's population as a whole generated 614.0 bed days per year per 1,000, *Figure 10.*

Figure 10.

Annual Bed Days Generated By 1,000 Population, California, 1993

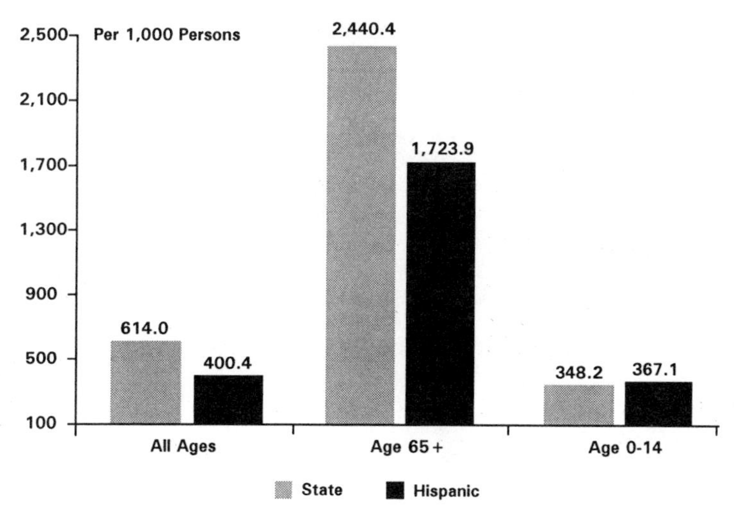

Source: Hospital Discharge Summary Machine Readable File

In part, this lower rate of hospitalization is related to the crude death rates detailed above. A younger population will have fewer heart attacks, cancers or strokes than an older population, and for the time being, the Latino population is much younger than the state as a whole. However, when the elderly population is considered by itself (age 65 and over) elderly Latinos generate fewer bed days (1,723.9) per 1,000 as compared to the state as a whole (2,440.4).

Data from Los Angeles County indicate that Latino elderly do not seem to suffer adverse health consequence from this lower hospitalization profile. The Latino elderly have much lower age-specific death rates for heart, cancer and stroke, and longer life expectancy. Given that health insurance coverage (Medicare) is available to most elderly, it is not clear to what extent the lower Latino elderly hospital use is a function of lower

Medicare enrollment (in spite of its nearly universal availability) and to what extent it is a function of overall health status.

While low hospital usage is in part a function of age, it must be remembered that the Latino high fertility rate generates a number of bed days for deliveries and newborns, and continuing need for hospitalizations for the many diseases and illnesses children experience. Thus, at the other end of the age spectrum, Latino children generate slightly more bed days (367.1) than the state figure (348.2).

Low Hospital Charges

Latinos generate lower per capita charges than the state figure. Overall, the average Latino generated $854 in hospital charges, while the average Californian generated $1,295, *Figure 11*. This lower figure needs to be viewed as a product of three dynamics, two of which (a younger population and lower rates of coverage) were discussed above. In addition, Latino hospitalizations are driven by relatively short term, relatively low cost deliveries, compared to the longer term, higher cost heart, cancer, and stroke-related costs.

Figure 11.

Average Annual Per Capita Hospital Charges, California, 1993

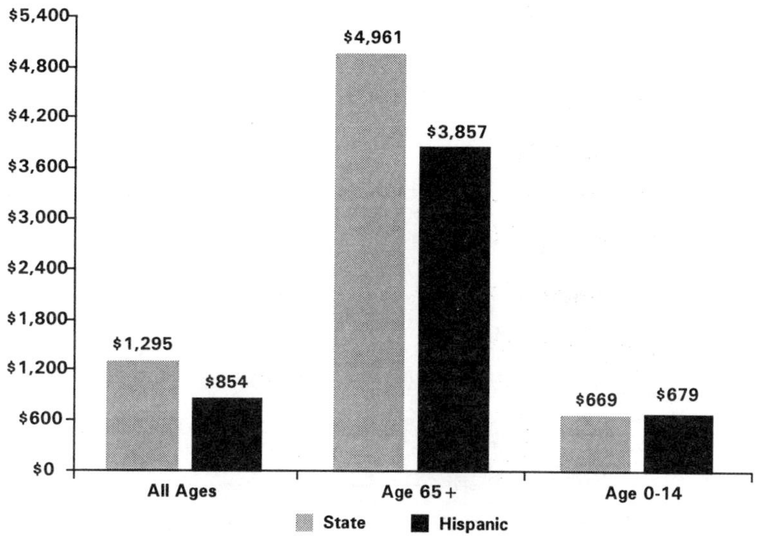

Source: Hospital Discharge Summary Machine Readable File

These low per capita averages are also seen in the elderly population, whereby Latino elderly generated $3,857 in charges, while the state's elderly generated $4,961. At the young end of the age scale, Latino children (birth to 14) generate slightly higher charges ($679) than the state per capita average ($669).

Different DRG Profiles

Latinos use hospital resources differently from the state norms, not only in the bed-days generated and charges generated, but also in the types of hospitalizations incurred.

We shall look at the top 20 reasons for hospitalizations, as defined by DRG codes. Each hospital must enter a code identifying the reason for the hospitalization. These codes are standardized and in use by every hospital and provide some uniform indicators of hospital utilization.

For these top 20 DRGs, the Latino reasons for hospitalizations, and rates, diverge markedly from the state figures. *Figure 12* provides illustration of the state's rate of hospital discharge per 1,000 population per year for the DRGs rank-ordered from 3 through 12, compared to Latino rates of hospital discharges per 1,000 Latino population per year.

Figure 12.

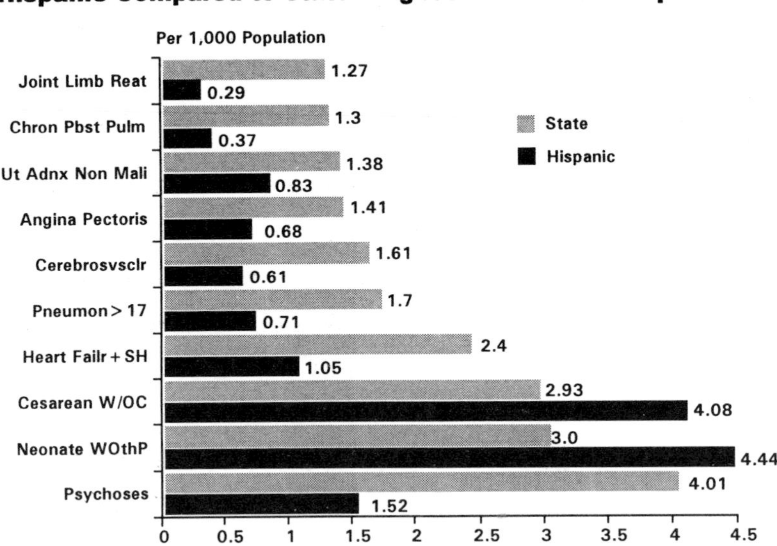

Source: Hospital Discharge Summary Machine Readable File

The two most common DRGs for both the state and for the Latino public are Normal Newborns and Vaginal Delivery without Complications. The Latino rate of 18.2 is higher than the state rate of 11.9 for Normal Newborns. Likewise, the Latino rate for Vaginal Delivery without Complications is higher than the state rate. Because of the large number of these relatively low-cost hospitalizations their inclusion in the chart so overshadow the other more expensive reasons for hospitalizations, that the distinctions become difficult to see, therefore these two are not shown in *Figure 12.*

Overall, the pattern is that Latinos have higher rates of hospitalizations for delivery and child-related DRGs, with rates around 25% higher than the state figure. However, for the other types of hospitalizations not birth or child-related, such as psychoses, heart failure plus shock, cerebrovascular process, joint and limb reattachment, etc., the Latino rates are about 75% lower.

Payment Source

While the medical market is currently driven by changes developed in the private sector, public financing is still an important part of hospitalizations. Public financing accounts for approximately two-thirds, or 68.9%, of the charges generated by Latinos while for the state in general, public financing accounts for 63.1%.

MediCare and Medi-Cal

Reflecting the younger age structure of the Latino population compared to the state, Latinos generated few lower per capita charges through Medicare ($153 per capita per year) than the average Californian ($497). And, in contrast, Latinos generated greater per capita Medi-Cal charges ($412 per year) than did the state as a whole ($285), *Figure 13.*

Figure 13.

Per Capita Medicare and Medi-Cal Charges, California, 1993

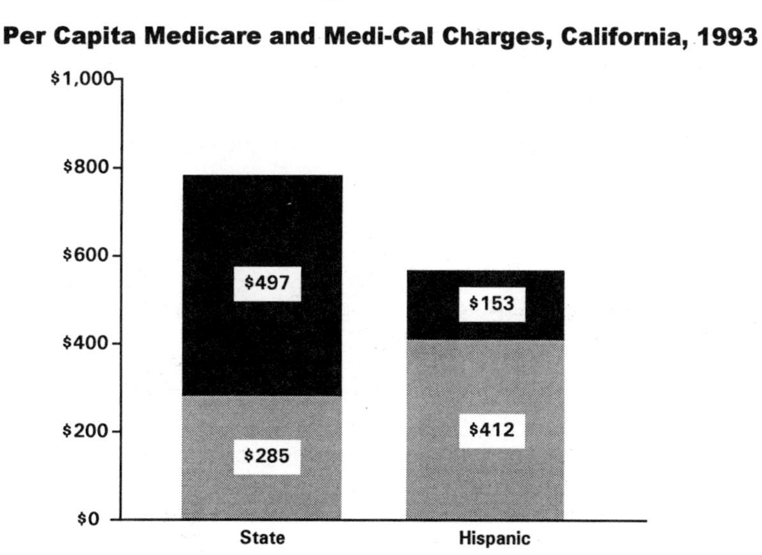

Source: Hospital Discharge Summary, Machine Readable File

All told, on a per capita basis, the average Latino generated $589 in publicly funded hospital charges ($153 charged to Medicare and $412 to Medi-Cal and the remainder to a number of other public programs), compared to the $817 generated by the average Californian ($497 charged to Medicare and $285 to Medi-Cal with the remainder from other public programs).

I. Health Insurance Coverage

As mentioned above, an undetermined portion of this differential hospitalization is due to lower levels of access to health insurance coverage. Hospital discharge data only tell us of those who were hospitalized, which is a small portion of the general population. The data do not tell us anything about the other 92.5% who were not hospitalized.

A quick glance at some studies indicate that Latinos have the lowest rate of hospital insurance coverage. Brown et al.,[5] have shown that in Los Angeles County, a much higher percent of Latinos do not have health insurance coverage. This higher rate of no insurance coverage will have some undetermined effect on both hospital utilization and ambulatory care usage.

A slightly earlier state level study (Hurtado, Hayes-Bautista, Valdez, and Hernandez, 1992[6]) indicates differential patterns of insurance coverage within the Latino population. Immigrants were least likely to have access to insurance coverage, even though employed (53%), while third-generation Latinos (the grandchildren of immigrants) had coverage levels (78%) only slightly lower than the state norm, *Figure 14*.

Figure 14.

Health Insurance Coverage For Employed Hispanic Adults By Nativity, California, 1993

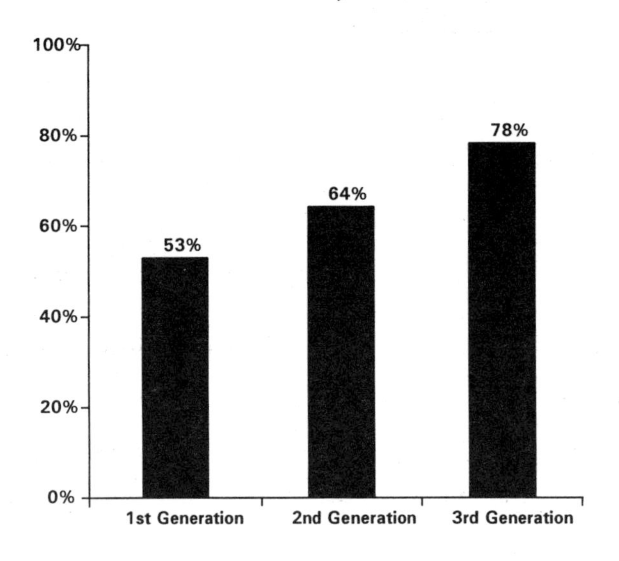

Source: Hurtado et al., 1992

J. Health Professional Supply

There are no reliable, comprehensive data on the ethnic breakdown of licensed, practicing health professionals in the state. Because there are no comprehensive figures for licensed, practicing Latino health professionals (physicians, dentists, nurses, etc.), the enrollment and graduation figures will have to provide an order-of-magnitude estimate.

Medical School

Prior to 1970, a Latino medical student was a rarity in the state. Beginning in that year, the state's medical schools made a conscientious effort to recruit and admit Latino medical students. In 1970, Latinos were 10.7% of the state's population, and Latino medical students were 7.0% of medical school enrollment, figures not too far from parity. However, while the Latino population tripled in size to be 25.6% of the state's population in 1990, Latino medical school enrollments remained around the 10.0% level, *Figure 15.*

Figure 15.

Percent Hispanic of Population and Medical School Graduates, California, 1970–1993

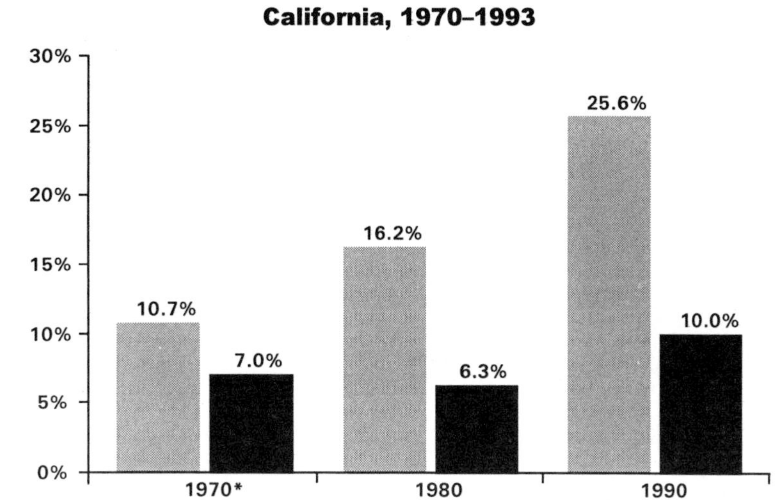

Source: Association of American Medical Colleges

In effect, there are fewer Latino medical students per Latino population in 1990 than there were in 1970. To fill part of that need, there has been a small, but important, influx of foreign-born, foreign-trained providers.

K. Overview of Health Profile

The Latino public in California shows a health status profile that is somewhat enigmatic, and poses both challenges and opportunities for health care policy, programs and providers in the 21st century. In a paradoxical way, although Latinos have the least access to care, they exhibit some very strong mortality indicators. However, the question of illnesses presents a different portrait. Communicable diseases are much more prevalent among the Latino public than in the general population. A preliminary reading of the hospital discharge data would indicate that hospitalizations for some conditions, such as asthma and juvenile pneumonia, are about 50% higher among Latinos than in the state. These are hospitalizations that, with proper ambulatory care, could be prevented.

3. Latino Health

A. Race, Culture and Society

Race

It appears as if race has re-emerged in the 1990s as a major variable in social thought attempting to describe differences between various groups in the country's public. The recent book, *The Bell Curve* (Herrnstein and Murray, 1994[7]) has brought back to the public discourse the school of thought that genetics play the determining role in differential behavior. A portion of medical thought has focused on the relationship between certain types of illnesses (e.g. sickle-cell anemia, Tay-Sachs disease) and certain types of genetic background.

In this new public discourse about race and behavior, Latinos offer an interesting alternative perspective. When used as an explanatory variable (as in Herrnstein and Murray), "race" is assumed to be a monolithic, homogeneous, unvarying quantity (this assumption has a history in this country's legal definition of racial groups for the assignment of societal benefits and/or sanctions). As a group, the Latino public of California essentially defies racial categorization, for it is fundamentally in its racial construction what would be considered a "mixed race" population, with a nearly bewildering degree of genetic variation. As a product of the fusion of Amerindian, European, African and Asian ancestry, it would be difficult to explain Latino behavior and health status by recourse to any concept which posits race as a uniform variable.

Thus, an understanding of the Latino health profile requires a better understanding of culture rather than race.

Culture

Much early work done on Latinos, health and culture focused on what were termed "cultural barriers" that supposedly impeded the proper use of health care services. In essence, Latino usage of Spanish and emphasis on family were considered characteristics that impeded utilization of modern medical care.

However, now that the focus of genetic prevention has shifted to diseases which are greatly influenced by lifestyle, the issue of culture takes on a different importance. The health profile of Latinos is at odds with what one would expect for a population with low income and education. It would be inappropriate to attempt to explain the health profile by assuming a uniform genetic background. The major explanatory variable which has yet to be fully explored is that of culture.

The culture of the Latino public is both very dynamic and very stable. It is itself the product of many different inputs, and has experienced vast, fundamental changes from 1492 to date. In terms of health, the culture of the Latino public is far more complex than a simple belief in a few folk illnesses such as "susto" (fright) or evil eye.

In fashions that yet remain to be explored, Latino culture is a major explanatory variable for the seemingly paradoxical health outcomes outlined above. This culture is shared by the 8.9 million persons in this public, and is forming a significant portion of the state's larger public culture.

Constant Growth

In 1940, Latinos were a fairly small minority group residing inside a state with a fairly small population. Out of the state's total population of 6.6 million, the 374,000 Latinos represented less than 6% of the state's total population.

During the post-World War II era, while the state's population grew, largely fueled by immigrants from other states, the Latino population grew at rates slightly higher than the state's rate. The growth came from such a small numeric base that by the time California's population was larger than that of the state of New York (1963), the Latino population had quadrupled in size, but represented only 9% of the state's total. Latino population growth in this period was largely driven by fertility, as immigration was severely restricted. There was a large Mexican guest-farm-worker population (the *braceros*), but they were not immigrants as they were not allowed to remain in the state nor to form families here.

In the mid 1960s, four events occurred independently, but simultaneously, that were to be decisive in the formation of California's public in the 1990s: 1) the ending of the Baby Boom period in the White population; 2) a sharp decrease of immigrants coming to the state from other parts of the country such as the Midwest; 3) the end of the *bracero* program; and, 4) the changing of immigration law.

With the end of the Baby Boom in the White population, White fertility rates dropped radically. Latino fertility rates had always been higher than White, even during the Baby Boom period. While White rates dropped, Latino rates continued to increase until the 1990s. Coupled with the slowdown in the numbers of in-migrants moving in from out of state, White growth slowed considerably, leading to very little population growth from 1970 to the present.

The ending of the *bracero* program, coupled with changes in immigration law that encouraged the reunification of families, and the continuing need for Mexican labor, led to increases in immigration from the mid 1960s to the present. Immigrant Latinos have higher fertility rates than U.S.-born Latinos, hence the overall birthrate for Latinos increased rather than decreased.

The Latino population grew even more rapidly than it had, from 2.1 million in 1970 to an estimated 8.9 million at present. That this growth occurred in a period of very low White population growth only made it seem even more evident than the earlier growth. Currently, nearly one out of every three Californians is Latino; in Los Angeles County, nearly one out of every two residents is Latino.

Increased Immigrant Presence

During the postwar era, the Latino population was largely U.S.-born (over 80%). The arrival of immigrants changed this composition, so that by 1990, nearly half the population was immigrant (44.7%), *Figure 16.*

Figure 16.

Hispanic Population Percent Immigrant, California, 1940–1990

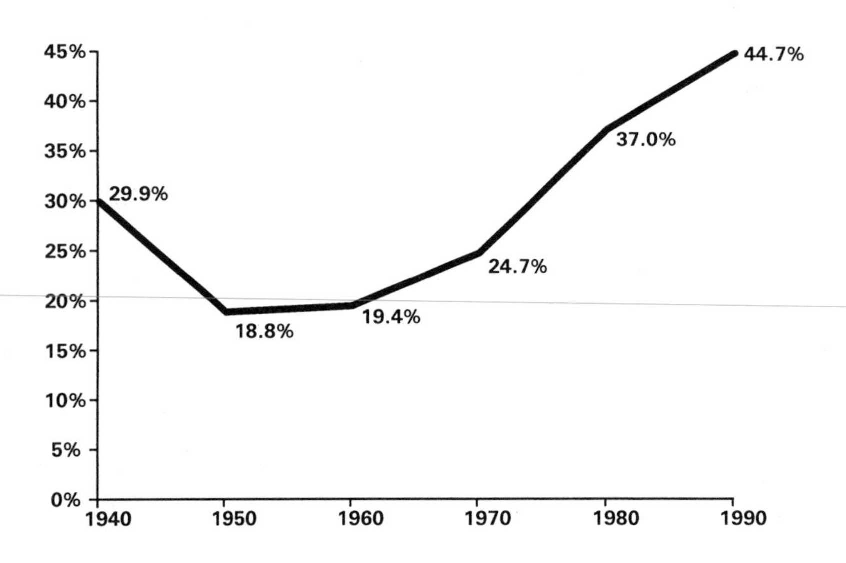

Source: 1940–1990 Census Public Use Microdata Samples

As a result, the majority of Latino households (80.3%) are now Spanish-speaking. As children are rarely immigrants, the presence of immigrants is felt even more in the adult population, 59.6% of Latino adults age 25 and over are immigrant.

The effects of such a large immigrant population are felt in all aspects of Latino community life, from increased prevalence of Spanish-language media to very specific health behaviors and outcomes.

Increased Heterogeneity

In addition to growing in size, the Latino population has become, in some key ways, more heterogeneous. While in the post-war period it was largely U.S.-born of Mexican origin, it has become more immigrant and non-Mexican. With the political upheavals and civil wars in Central America, the 1980s saw an outpouring of population from

El Salvador, Guatemala, Nicaragua and other countries south of Mexico. In 1990, nearly one out of every five Latinos (19.7%) was from non-Mexican, largely Central American origin. Less than 3% of the Latino population is Cuban or Puerto Rican, hence the national pattern of reporting in detail on these two populations is not appropriate for this state (although it is for the national level).

In addition to heterogeneity by immigration and country of origin, Latinos are also more heterogeneous by the emergence of a sizeable middle-class. While the percent of the Latino population that is high income and high education is still lower than in the general population, it is a sizeable population (numbering more than 1 million adults). That number represents nearly one out of every three Latino adults, and is growing at a rate nearly twice that of the general population.

Increased Homogeneity

In a seemingly paradoxical fashion, Latinos are also experiencing an increased homogeneity in certain key areas. Linguistically, Spanish is much more present in the Latino population than it was in the postwar years. While Spanish advertising was virtually nonexistent in the post-WWII era, it is today the most cost-effective way to reach large segments of the Latino market.

Driven by the increased linguistic homogeneity around the Spanish language, a communications shell has developed, creating greater ease and effectiveness in reaching that market. In the early 1960s there were virtually no means of communicating with Latinos, which, coupled with small numbers, made it necessary to apply "rare population sampling" techniques in order to carry out epidemiological or educational programs and activities. Now, numerous television networks, dozens of radio stations, and literally hundreds of newspapers and magazines stitch together the Latino community, providing a homogeneity of taste, opinion and discourse that was unknown in the early 1940s and 1950s.

Youthfulness

Factors such as high birth rates and young adult immigration combine to make the Latino population very young. Thirty-two percent of the Latino population consists of children 18 years and under, in the non-Latino population, that figure is 20.0%.

As a result of this youthfulness, Latinos are over-represented in the child population and under-represented in the elderly. One out of every three children in the state is Latino, while less than one out of every ten elderly is Latino.

B. Obstructive Factors

Low Educational Attainment

A lower percent of Latino adults (age 25 and over) have graduated from high school, attended college or graduated from college, than adults of any other group. Overall, 45.2% of Latino adults graduated from high school compared to 76.2% of the entire state's adult population.

This low educational attainment level is most pronounced among the immigrant poplation. While 66.5% of U.S.-born Latino adults were high school graduates, only 30.7% of Immigrant Latino adults were also high school graduates. Likewise, a lower percent of Latinos attend college (26.3%) than the state's average (53.9%). U.S.-born Latinos are more likely to attend college (39.2%) than immigrant Latinos (17.4%). Similarly, a lower percentage of Latino adults are college graduates (7.1%) than is the state's average (23.3%). Again, the U.S.-born Latino adults are more likely to be college graduates (10.0%) than immigrant Latino adults (5.0%), *Figure 17.*

Figure 17.

Hispanic Educational Attainment, California, 1990

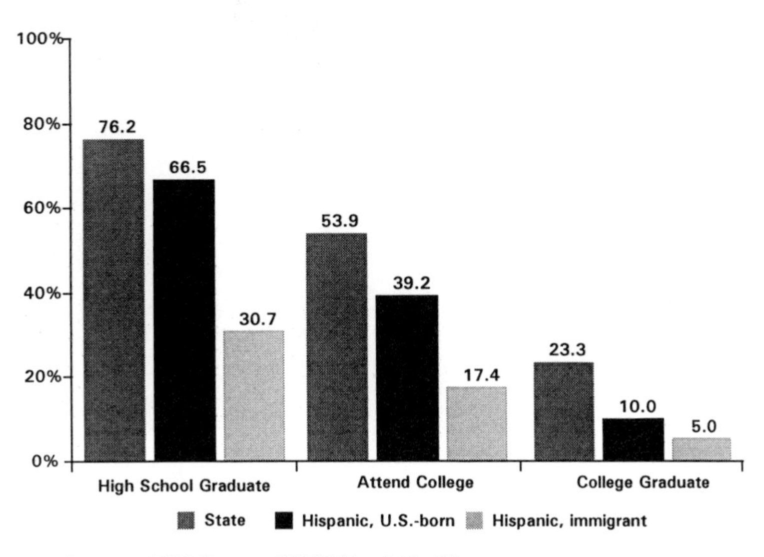

Source: 1990 Census PUMS Readable File

Lower Income

Latinos have much lower household income than other groups. Overall, adults in the state average $44,126 annual income. Latinos generally averaged $33,736.

There was a noticeable difference between U.S.-born and immigrant Latinos. U.S.-born Latinos had higher household incomes, $37,466 as compared to the $30,865 received by immigrant Latinos, *Figure 18*.

Figure 18.

Hispanic Household Income, California, 1990

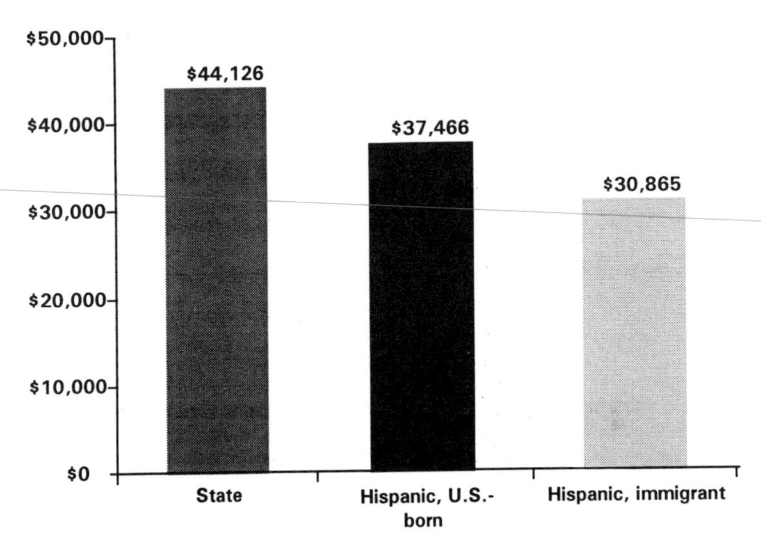

Source: 1990 Census PUMS Machine Readable File

High Poverty

As a result of lower educational attainment and the inability to earn a higher wage, Latinos were more likely to live in poverty. Overall, 10.5% percent of California's adults live in poverty, while 18.5% of Latino adults do.

And again, there is a marked difference between U.S.-born and immigrant Latinos. The poverty level of U.S.-born Latinos was much lower, at 12.4%, than the 22.9% of immigrant Latinos, *Figure 19*.

Figure 19.

Percent Hispanic Adults in Poverty, California, 1990

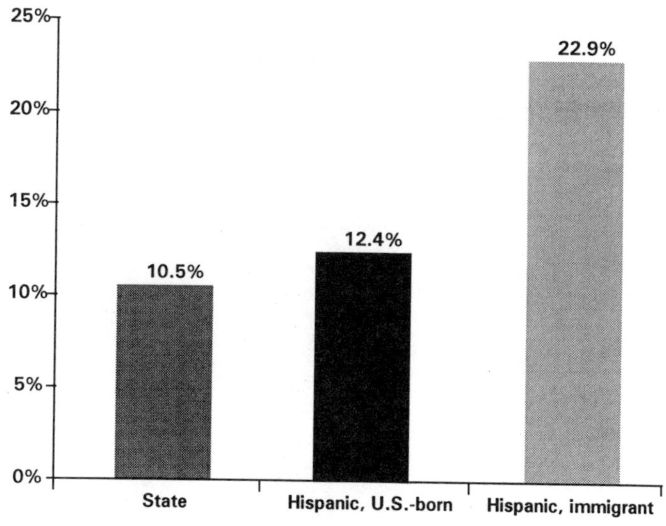

25%
20%
15%
10%
5%
0%

State	Hispanic, U.S.-born	Hispanic, immigrant
10.5%	12.4%	22.9%

Source: 1990 Census PUMS Machine Readable File

In short, in key characteristics such as income and educational attainment, Latinos find a number of obstacles that yield lower income and lower educational attainment than is the average for the state.

C. Enabling Processes

In spite of these factors, there are other enabling processes that are characteristics of Latino adults.

High Male Labor Force Participation

Compared to the average for the state, Latinos have a higher male labor force participation, 83.1% of Latino males participated in the labor force, compared to 78.0% for the state.

Within this high labor force participation, immigrant Latino males have a higher rate (86.3%) than U.S.-born Latino males (78.2%), *Figure 20.*

Figure 20.

Percent Hispanic Male 16+, Labor Force Participation, California, 1990

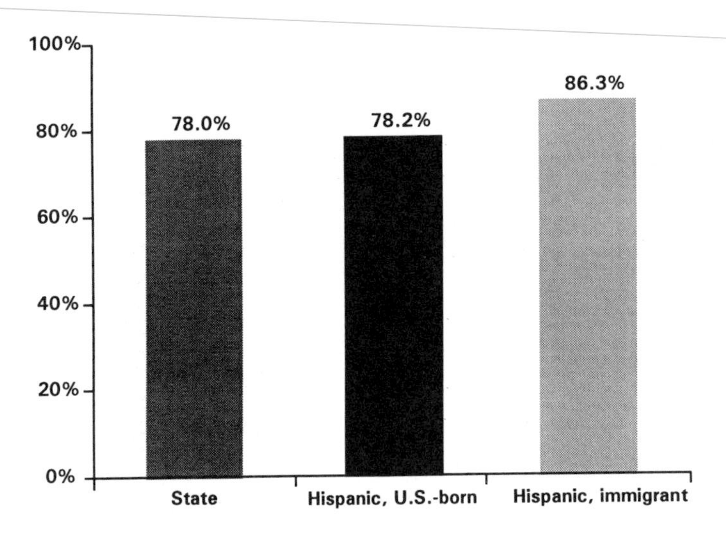

Source: 1990 Census PUMS Machine Readable File

Percent Employed

In order to participate in the labor force, one must either be employed, or unemployed but looking for work. Latinos have a higher percent employed (75.3%) than the state average (73.0%)

Immigrant Latinos are more likely to be employed (78.9%) than U.S.-born Latino males (70.9).

Low Labor Force Desertion

Latinos are less likely to leave the labor force (16.8%) than the state average for males (22.0%). Immigrants were much less likely to leave the labor force (13.7%) than U.S.-born Latinos (21.8%).

Higher Unemployment

While more likely to be employed or be in the labor force, Latinos also have a higher rate of unemployment (7.9%) than the state average (5.0%). Immigrants have higher unemployment (8.3%) than U.S.-born Latinos (7.3%).

Strong Family Formation

Latino households are much more likely to be composed of the classic couple with children (41.1%) as compared to the average for the state (26.0%).

Immigrant Latino households are more likely (49.0%) to be composed of couple with children than U.S.-born Latino households (31.0%), *Figure 21.*

Figure 21.

Hispanic Household Type: Couples with Children, California, 1990

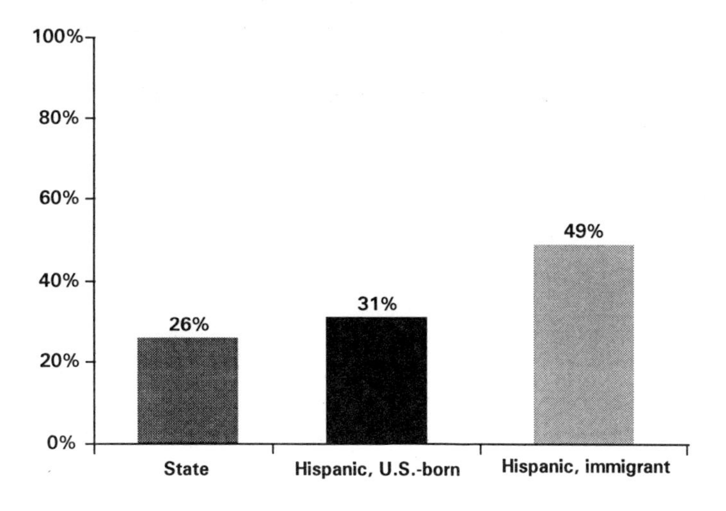

Source: 1990 Census PUMS Machine Readable File

Low Public Assistance

Recent political campaigns have emphasized the image that immigrant Latinos are drawn to this state to enroll in welfare benefits. Latino immigrants, when controlled for poverty, actually receive Public Assistance at much lower rates (18.5%) than U.S.-born Latinos (55.4%) or the state average (49.1%), *Figure 22.*

Figure 22.

Hispanic Adult (16+) Public Assistance to Poverty Ratio, California, 1990

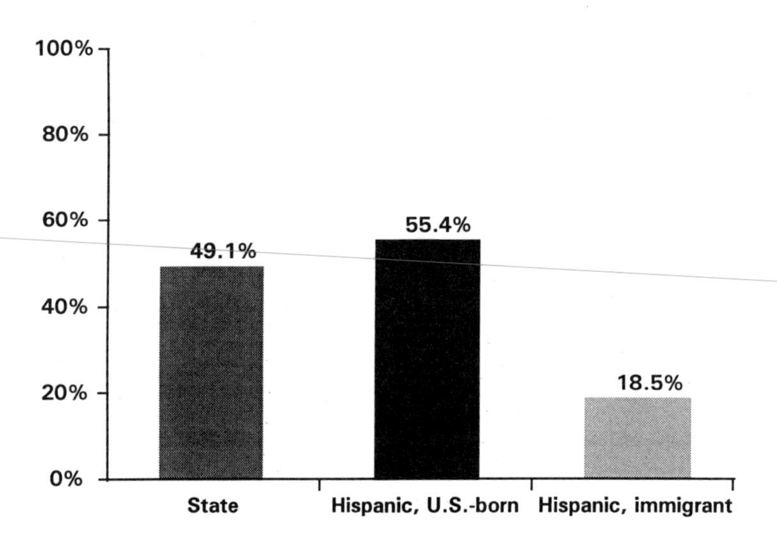

Source: 1990 Census PUMS Machine Readable File

4. The Latino Epidemiological Paradox

A. Strengths, Weaknesses, Opportunities & Threats (SWOT) Analysis

Some bases for strategic planning for the health of the Latino public may be discerned via a SWOT analysis. This is a process which creates a listing of the Strengths, Weaknesses, Opportunities and Threats.

Strengths

1. *Continued market growth:* This public will continue to grow as a market through the end of the decade and on into the 21st century. This growth will be due to both births and immigration.
2. *Sociodemographic behavior of immigrants:* The immigrant portion of the Latino public exhibit a profile that represents continuing contributions to the state's economy and society.
3. *Strong health profile overall:* Should be considered a strength, as long as it is properly managed.

Weaknesses

1. *Poverty:* High levels of poverty in spite of high labor force participation.
2. *Low insurance coverage:* Low rates of health insurance coverage through either public or private means.

Opportunities

1. *Family and preventive care focus:* The Latino public appears to be well suited for the current shifting of emphasis of medicine and health care services to preventive and family-focused care.

2. *Population suited for managed care:* Such organizations in particular may find a tremendous opportunity to enroll an increasing market once an appropriate cost and pricing structure is developed that builds upon the Latino health profile.

3. *Maintain a healthy profile:* A major opportunity for health care delivery organizations is to be found in the maintenance of the currently relatively healthy profile.

Threats

1. *Exclusionary political discourse:* The current political discourse about the Latino public tends to be couched in exclusionary terms. Political decisions such as Proposition 187 have the overt purpose of decreasing the Latino public's participation (or, at the least, a perceived significant portion of the Latino public) in the state's public sector society, especially education and health care. Restrictive language policies have the same overt purpose.

2. *Latino market denial:* Until recently, many large providers of care had overlooked the Latino market by using a "dysfunctional minority" perspective, and the Latino market was seen as undesirable. This perspective may be changing, (ride the aggressive advertising campaigns of some HMOs and insurers).

3. *Not culturally competent care:* Successful management of the health of the Latino public will require a level of cultural competence that is not yet in place. Management of "lifestyle" diseases require a thorough understanding of Latino health attitudes, beliefs and behaviors that are not currently a large part of the training and education of health care providers at all levels.

4. *Erosion in behaviors over time:* This was most noticeable in the sociodemographic indicators, the immigrant had stronger levels of labor force participation and family formation than the U.S.-born Latino. This is a consistent trend. Health indicators are spottier, but numerous smaller studies have indicated that U.S.-born Latinos tend to drink more, smoke more, use drugs more, and have higher infant mortality than immigrant Latinos.

B. Latinos In 2015

By 2015, Latinos will most likely be the largest single public in the state (although not a majority) numbering between 15 million and 20 million.

Yet, while the largest group, it will not be a monolithic group. Indeed, Latinos will continue to be a "fuzzy-edged" group, without clear-cut racial boundaries. "Latino-ness" will continue to be defined more by attitudes, values and behavior rather than purported genetic background.

C. Strategic Recommendations

The California Endowment mission has two main goals:

- Increase access to health care for underserved individuals and communities;
- Create fundamental improvements in the health status of California's public.

The following recommendations are designed to assist the implementation of these two goals with the 8.9 million strong Latino public of California. These recommendations are at different levels.

D. Service Level Recommendations

1. Patient education

The ability of providers statewide to access Latino-normed educational materials for style-of-life disease prevention needs to be increased.

a. Material clearinghouse

Establish a single-source clearinghouse for Latino-normed patient education materials accessible to all providers. Some materials have been developed by specific agencies (e.g. American Cancer Society), usually in categorical areas (e.g. cancer, AIDS, tobacco control, etc.). Other materials have been developed in academic settings, and are not available outside the academic literature. Establish the clearinghouse to collect and disseminate such materials, which should be accessible via an 800-number and an Internet World Wide Web page.

b. Technical assistance

Patient education materials require constant, ongoing development and updating. A technical assistance service needs to be established by which a network of academics and experienced providers can provide ongoing technical assistance in the development and updating of materials.

2. Cultural Competency Training

Providers need training in cultural competency, to learn how to best deliver care to a Latino patient base. A series of training sessions can be provided that prepare providers with the appropriate knowledge, motivations, and skills. Such training should provide continuing education credits for those providers with an annual hours requirement for licensure renewal.

3. Community Consortia

Establish action-oriented consortia in those areas where Latinos are at risk (e.g. communicable diseases, asthma, homicide, teenage pregnancy, etc.). The consortia would be charged with the responsibility to develop statewide initiatives for each risk area. An example of such a consortium is the Roybal Elderly Immunization project of East Los Angeles.

4. Prenatal/Early Childhood

This needs to be a primary focus for services as this is the entree to medical care utilization. While this is not currently a high-risk area for Latino newborns, the low levels of prenatal care would suggest a serious disconnect between the service providers and the Latina population. A special consortium needs to be established to create statewide programs to define appropriate levels of service and increase access to them.

5. Pilot programs in managed care with Latino member base

While medical economics appear to be drawing larger percentages of the population into managed care, very little is known of the effects of managed care on a Latino enrolled base, nor of the effects of a Latino enrolled base on the structure and functioning of managed care. Pilot projects need to be developed that will provide indicators of these mutual effects as quickly as possible.

E. Education Level Recommendations

1. Curriculum development in Latino Health

There is very little information available and virtually no organized curriculum in Latino health for health professional training programs. Organized curriculum "modules" need to be developed that present the basic information about Latino health and its management. These modules need to provide guidance for instructional efforts (academic and professional) that wish to focus on Latino health. Modules need to be developed in a number of substantive areas (e.g. patient compliance, asthma, epidemiology, etc.). Each module should consist of lecture outline, reading materials, graphics, and (when appropriate) instructional video or CD-ROM material.

2. **Continuing Medical Education**

   Opportunities for Continuing Medical Education (CME), Continuing Nursing Education and Continuing Dental Education need to be offered to those providers who wish to fulfill their CME requirements by increasing their knowledge of the management of health of Latino patient base.

3. **Public Information Fora**

   These would be an opportunity to share research findings with the state's public.

4. **Executive Education**

   Preparation in Latino health needs to be provided to top level policy makers, political decision makers, executives of agencies and hospitals about the health of multicultural California.

F. Research Level Recommendations

1. **New Research Models**

   While historically the health of Latino and minority populations has been based on the "dysfunctional minority" model, it is now time to begin to develop new models that build upon the strengths seen in the various groups. A new body of theoretical models could be developed under the label of "asset optimization models" in which culture is linked to health in a proactive way, rather than as a barrier.

   These new models, once developed, can provide a knowledge base for programs and policies designed to create fundamental improvements in the health of the California multicultural public.

2. Data Files Creation

Lack of data has slowed down development of new theoretical models. While data about Latinos and minorities have been collected since the late 1970s to the early 1980s, very little of these data have been analyzed or made available to the general public. Annual data files for Latino status and behavior need to be created, using already collected data (e.g. vital statistics, hospital discharge, birth outcome, Census data, Current Population Survey, etc.) as well as annual updates as soon as data are available.

3. New Primary Data Collection

There are many areas of Latino health status and behavior that have not been well researched. In particular, the change to "high level wellness" orientations points to the need for new primary data sets that will allow for better policy and program development. Areas that need data quickly include: managed care; clinical issues; social relations and diet; physical exercise; early breast cancer detection; substance use and abuse; violence; and teenage pregnancy.

4. Dissemination Effort

Regular release of data and information via periodical publications and via electronic distribution needs to be facilitated.

G. Policy Level Recommendations

1. Create Shared Societal Vision

Policy discussions in many arenas of the state—health, education, employment, welfare, economic, business development—are hampered by the lack of a common vision of a multicultural public in the state of California. Many high-profile issues such as undocumented immigration, affirmative action, bilingual education, English only and others are currently debated as "win-lose" propositions, with no middle ground solutions being posited. There is danger of a spillover of ethnic "gridlock" discussions stemming from these higher profile issues to lower profile ones, such as access of pregnant mothers and children to adequate prenatal care. By using a focus on the health of the state's public, it will be possible to develop and articulate a comprehensive vision of the state as a single public with many members, rather than many members with little in common.

To the extent that The California Endowment could foster this via work in multicultural health, all sectors of the state could benefit.

2. New Assumptions in Health Policy

Much policy discussion about multicultural health is based on the assumption of minority dysfunction, with programs proposed which are remedial in nature. The assumption of minority dysfunction tends to undergird policy debates in other sectors, such as criminal justice, education, housing and others.

The California Endowment could foster activities that would create new policy assumptions based on data that allow for a more positive, functional view of a multicultural society.

3. Financing

As access to health care is facilitated by financing mechanisms, these must be appropriate for the Latino public. While in the past it has often been assumed that minorities are best reached through public sector programs, the Latino profile of high labor force participation in private sector jobs must be taken into account. A better understanding of Latino occupation and industry patterns is needed.

4. Managed Care

The movement to managed care has taken place without full consideration of the effects of managed care on the Latino public, nor the effects of the Latino public on managed care. A preliminary overview of the data presented earlier suggests that the growing Latino public would have many effects on a managed care system.

The California Endowment should support activities that provide a full exploration of the mutual effects of the movement to managed care and the growing Latino public.

5. Health Promotion and Disease Prevention

The concept of health promotion needs to be expanded so that it automatically includes Latino and other minority publics.

Figures

Endnotes

[1] Becerra, J.E.; Hague, C.S.; Atrash, H.K; Perez, N., 1991. Infant mortality among Hispanics. JAMA 265: 217-21.

[2] Becerra, J.E.; Hague, C.S.; Atrash, H.K; Perez, N., 1991. Infant mortality among Hispanics. JAMA 265: 217-21.

[3] Vega et al., 1993

[4] National Center for Health Statistics, 1994. Current Estimates from the National Health Interview Survey, 1993. Hyattsville, MD DHHS Publication No. (PHS) 95-1518.

[5] Brown, E. Richard. 1992. Task Force for Health Care Access in Los Angeles County. Presented to the Los Angeles County Board of Supervisors.

[6] Hurtado, Aida; Hayes-Bautista, David E.; Valdez, R. Burciaga; Hernandez, Anthony. 1992. Redefining California: Latino Social Engagement and Social Policy. Los Angeles, University of Southern California, Los Angeles: Chicano Studies Research Center

[7] Herrnstein, Rechard J.; Murray, Charles A. 1994. The Bell Curve: Intelligence and Class Structure in American Life. New York: The Free Press.